An Easy

Written by
Elizabeth Dale

Illustrated by
Natalie Smith

Ransom

Ben was happy. He was babysitting.

It was an easy job.

"I can't sleep," said Anna.
"Mummy lets me have a biscuit."

"No she doesn't. Go back to bed,"
said Ben.

Anna went back to bed.

Ben watched TV.

"I can't sleep," said Anna.
"Mummy lets me have a drink."

"No she doesn't. Go back to bed,"
said Ben.

Anna went back to bed.

Ben watched TV again.

"I can't sleep," said Anna.
"Mummy lets me bounce down the stairs."

"No she doesn't. Go back to bed," said Ben.

Anna went back to bed.

Ben watched TV again.

"I can't sleep," said Anna. "Mummy lets me play."

"No she doesn't. Go back to bed," said Ben.

Anna went back to bed.

Ben watched TV again.

"I can't sleep," said Anna.
"Mummy lets me watch TV."

Ben was not happy. He wanted
to watch TV.

"OK," he said.

So Anna watched TV with Ben.

"Mummy lets me bounce on her knee at TV time," said Anna.

"No she doesn't," said Ben.

"Mummy lets me eat her chocolate at TV time," said Anna.

"No she doesn't," said Ben.

"Mummy lets me drink her drink at TV time," said Anna.

"No she doesn't," said Ben.

"Mummy lets me draw on her face at TV time," said Anna.

"No she doesn't," said Ben.

They heard the front door slam.

"Mummy!" cried Anna.

Anna rushed upstairs to bed.

"Hello, Ben," said Anna's mum. "Was Anna good?"

"Yes," said Ben. "Anna was very good. She didn't wake up once. I am very good at babysitting."